Look and Find®

OLIVIA™

pi kids® publications international, ltd.

When Olivia plays dress-up with Francine, she likes to wear anything that's red! Search Olivia's room to find some of her favorite accessories.

Tutu

Bow

Purse

Beret

Scarf

Tiara

Glasses

The great painter Olivia has completed many works of art. But what will her next great masterpiece be? Look around the museum for these paintings that might inspire her.

Olivia shines on opening night. Look around the theater to find some of her co-stars who will help the show be a smash hit.

When Olivia decides to set up a lemonade stand, she has plenty of lemonade, but no glasses! Look around to help Olivia find some cups for her customers.

Sport bottle

White mug

Glass

Glass jar

Yellow cup

Red cup

Blue mug

Sippy cup

When Olivia feeds the sea lions, she thinks of every detail! Search the sea for these other creatures that might like a snack.

Puffer fish

This fish

Sea star

Stingray

Crab

Sea turtle

Squid

Seahorse

On show-and-tell day, Olivia brought her pet cat, Edwin. Search the classroom for these other pets that are visiting school today.

Cat

Dog

Frog

Fish

Snake

Squirrel

Bird

Hamster

"Attention, shoppers!" When Olivia goes to the supermarket, she pretends to be the manager. Take a look around her store to find these fruits.

Bananas

Apple

Peach

Pineapple

Orange

Grapes

Blueberries

10¢

Sale!

Olivia has fun building sand sculptures at the beach. Look around for these buildings she made with her friends.

Igloo

The Leaning Tower of Pisa

The Eiffel Tower

Olivia's house

The Chrysler Building

The Great Pyramid

Fairy-tale castle

In her imagination, Olivia travels to many faraway places. Go back to her bedroom to find these postcards.

Tokyo

Istanbul

Sydney

Moscow

Cairo

Paris

Buenos Aires

Madrid

Hurry back to the art museum to find these art supplies that belong to Olivia.

Tray of water paints

This blank canvas

Palette

Paint spatula

Pencil

This paintbrush

Tube of oil paint

Return to the theater to find these props that Olivia might need.

Telephone

Parasol

Bouquet

Unicycle

Tiara

Book

Go back to Olivia's lemonade stand and point to these ingredients that she should not add to her lemonade!

Eggs

Oranges

Salt

Oil

Flour

Ketchup

Mayonnaise

Cereal

Dive back under the sea to find these items from the sunken ship.

A wooden chest

A pitcher

A goblet

A spyglass

A sword

An anchor

An old globe

Return to show-and-tell day to find these special treasures.

A dollhouse

A birdcage

An autographed baseball

A model airplane

A photo album

A skateboard

Roll back to the grocery store and search for these healthy vegetables.

Asparagus

Carrots

Celery

Green pepper

Eggplant

Corn on the cob

Broccoli

Go back to the beach to help Olivia find 20 seashells for her collection.